200 Questions
You Must Ask, Investigate
and Know Before you say,
'I DO'

Michael & Bernice Hutton-Wood

THE MANDATE:

'...SET IN ORDER THE THINGS THAT ARE OUT OF ORDER AND RAISE AND APPOINT LEADERS IN EVERY CITY.' - Titus 1:5

MICHAEL HUTTON-WOOD MINISTRIES
RELEASING POTENTIAL
- MAXIMIZING DESTINY

HOUSE OF JUDAH (PRAISE) MINISTRIES
&
LEADERS FACTORY INTERNATIONAL
RAISING GENERATIONAL LEADERS
- IMPACTING NATIONS

SIMPA:
SCEPTRE INTERNATIONAL MINISTERS
& PASTORS ASSOCIATION
EQUIPPING, EMPOWERING, COACHING, MENTORING AND PROVIDING COVERING FOR PASTORS, MINISTERS AND LEADERS ACROSS THE NATIONS!

THIS BOOK CONTAINS
For The Fresh Single Person

200 QUESTIONS
Every Single Person
Must Ask, Investigate and Know
Before They Say
'I DO'

For The Divorced Person, the Separated for one reason or the other
or the widowed considering Re-marriage
[Thinking of Getting Married Again]

200 QUESTIONS
Every Divorced Person
Must Ask, Investigate and Know
Before They Say
'I DO' AGAIN

Compiled For Your Preventive Benefit By:
The Pastors of House of Judah:

Bishop Michael Hutton-Wood
&
Pastor (Mrs.) Bernice Hutton-Wood

Unless otherwise indicated, all scriptural references are taken from
the King James
Version of the Bible.

200 Questions You Must Ask, Investigate and Know
Before You Say 'I Do'

ISBN 978-0-9539549-8-8
2nd Edition

Hutton-Wood publications
In the UK write to:
Michael Hutton-Wood Ministries
P. O. Box 1226, Croydon. CR9 6DG

Or in the UK
Call: Tel. 020 8689 6010; 07956 815 714
Outside the UK call: +44 20 8689 6010; +44 7956 815 714
Or contact: WEBSITE: www.houseofjudah.org.uk
Email: michaelhutton-wood@fsmail.net
houseofjudah@ymail.com
leadersfactoryinternational@yahoo.com

Published & distributed by: Michael Hutton-Wood Ministries
(Incorporating Hutton-Wood World Outreach Ministries)

Printed in the United Kingdom

CONTENTS

Dedication   6

Introduction   9

200 Questions You Must Ask, Investigate and Know   12
Before You Say 'I Do'

Poignant Reminders   73

DEDICATION

Dedicated To:
All Who Want To Avoid The Mistakes Of Previous Generations, Including
Ours.

Proverbs 4:7,

"Wisdom is the principal thing; therefore get wisdom: and with all thy getting get understanding."

'……….. IN ALL YOUR GETTING, GET UNDERSTANDING'

'Before you take a journey into marriage, ask! (An African Idiom)

'We are free up to the point of choice, then, the choice controls the chooser.'
- Mary Crowley

He who chooses the beginning of a road also chooses its outcome.

"Control your destiny or someone else will."
- Jack Welch, CEO
General Electric Company

WARNING:
Don't You Dare
Say
'I Do'
Until You Are
Fully Satisfied
With The Results
From These
Questions
And
Investigations

INTRODUCTION

We had some rough times in the initial stages of our marriage because we were ignorant of some of the contents of this book. We had no role model because we were both raised by single parents but for the grace of God and the following factors:

Our getting saved and studying God's word

Learning from our Seniors in ministry through teaching materials on audio tapes, cds, videos, dvds, conferences, mentoring, marriage seminars and a dogged determination to make it work we won't be here to write this book.

Our intention therefore is to make sure you don't go through what we went through to get to where we are today on our way to perfection. Be wise and receive counsel for scripture says in a multitude of counsel, there is safety.

Don't just jump into marriage; ask questions and receive crucial satisfying genuine answers with spiritual backing and discernment.

One of the major problems of our society has arisen because we live in a day in which many people do not bother to take the time to ask certain vital and crucial questions and investigate certain backgrounds to receive needed information before they get married.

We live in a day and hour when people just meet each other on the street and are sensually moved by what they see [men] and by what they hear [women] and immediately or not many days after that jump into a relationship and sometimes marriage. People who have only barely gotten to know each other then proceed to go to the jewellery stores and buy engagement rings and place it on the finger of the lady's without any form of consultation whatsoever. How dense can a person be to make such a decision and play with 'fire' and mess with God's program for humanity? How in the world can you enter such an institution that is meant to be for life without asking certain vital questions?

MARRIAGE IS AN INSTITUTION AND YOU DON'T JUST ENTER IN WILLYNILLY. The issues that arise from marriage are real and you need to ask real questions before you enter in. That is why these questions born out of feedback from various counselling sessions with both singles and married couples have been thoroughly investigated and compiled for those who want to enter into marriage and stay married until death do they part.

WHY THIS BOOK?

Because, we want people to know and adopt God's intention for marriage Scripture says, 'Therefore shall a man leave his Father and Mother and be joined unto his wife and they two shall be one flesh.' – live forever. (Genesis 2:24)

There is a key for a successful lifelong marriage and it is found in the mind of the manufacturer of marriage – GOD. It can be found in His Manual and Will for Successful Living – THE BIBLE. Go and live by the instructions from this source.
It shall be well with you. Shalom!

200 QUESTIONS
[INCLUDING TEACHING ON THE FOUR KINDS OF LOVE]

Your Personal Pre-Marital Counselling Questionnaire
[Prepared by Bishop Michael &
Pastor (Mrs.) Bernice Hutton-Wood]

[Carry this questionnaire yourself and fill it in as you go along. Answer these questions about your partner and yourself sincerely. Compare notes, discuss it, pray together about it and take it along with you for your counselling sessions with your Pastor or Pre- Marital Counsellor.]

QUESTIONS:

1. What is your name? [Your real name]; Have you changed your name other than through marriage? If yes why, and when?

....

....

....

....

....

2. How young or how old are you really?...

3. Where were you born? ....……………………………………..

…………………………………………………………..………….…..

4. Were your parents expecting a boy or a girl?

…………………………………………………......……………….......

…………………………………......………………………….......….…

5. Were you raised up by both parents [father and mother] in the same home, by a single parent, an aunt or uncle, foster parent or other relatives?

……………………………………………………………………….…..

……………………………………………………………………………

…………………………..……………

6. If raised by an aunt, an uncle, foster parent or others, how would you describe your relationship with them and theirs to you?

……………………………………………………………………….…..

…………………………………………………………………….………

…………………………………………………………………......………

………………………………………………………………………….…

……………………………………………………………………….……

………………………..……………

7. How close were you to your dad and by what name, nickname, or title did you call him?

…………………………………………………………………………..

………………………………………………………………………….…

………………………..……………

8. How would you describe your relationship with your father or the one who stood in as your dad whilst you were growing up?

....

....

....

....

....

....

9. How close were you to your mum and by what name or title did you call her?

....

....

....

....

....

....

10. How would you describe your relationship with your mother or the one who stood in as your mum whilst you were growing up?

....

....

....

11. Did they love you dearly and did they ever tell you sometimes often or not at all?

....

....

....

12. Did you love them and did you express it in words and action?

....

....

....

13. Were you an only child or one among many?

....

....

....

14. What were your childhood experiences like; good, bad exciting, memorable, one you would want to repeat or share with your children, or want them to experience as well or it was one you would rather forget?

....

....

....

....

....

....

15. Were your parents divorced or separated at any point in time? If yes, what were the reasons and consequences?

....

....

....

....

....

....

VERY SENSITIVE QUESTIONS

[You have an option to answer or not answer these questions. However, your sincere answers will enable you to be ministered to, helped and counselled better so that this history does not repeat itself in your future marriage relationship. There has been a tendency for those who've had this kind of experiences in the past to be cold towards their partner's show of love and affection or react wildly to any expression of anger.]

16. Were you abused in any way and if yes in what way? i.e. physically or sexually [Remember, you have an option to answer or not answer]

....

....

....

....

....

....

17. Were you abused by someone older than you or someone your own age or around your age?

....

....

....

....

....

18. How often was this abuse? ....

....

....

....

....

....

19. Was this at home or outside?

....

....

....

....

....

....

20. By relatives or neighbours?

....

....

....

21. How long did it go on for? ....

....

....

22. When did it stop?

....

....

....

....

23. How did you deal with or overcome this experience?

....

....

....

24. Was anyone hurt other than you from this experience?

....

....

....

25. Do you still remember the experience and what do you feel when you remember?

....

....

....

26. Are you still traumatised by that experience?

....

....

....

27. Has it in any way disturbed the way you relate to such people in life?

....

....

....

....

28. Has it made you defensive, cautious, careful, resentful or bitter towards such people or people of that age group?

....

....

....

29. What is your attitude towards love or family relationships?

....
....
....

30. Do you think that experience will in any way affect your affections or relationship with your partner?

....
....
....
....
....
....

31. What is your attitude towards men in general or women in general as a result of that experience?

....
....
....

32. What is your attitude towards grown men or grown women?

....
....
....

33. If you are a man, what do you react to most in women?

....
....
....

34. If you are a woman, what do you react to most in men?

....
....
....

35. What has been the most difficult experience that you have had in your life so far?

....

....

....

....

36. Do you accept the family in which you were born into?

....

....

....

37. What one thing would you like to see changed in your family?

....

....

....

....

38. When you think of your father, what thought comes to mind? [Such as happy memories, regrets, a blank or painful thoughts]?

....

....

....

....

39. When you think of your mother, what thought comes to mind? [Such as happy memories, regrets, a blank or painful thoughts]..................

....

....

....

40. Are you still walking in unforgiveness, bitterness, resentment, anger, hatred and seek revenge towards your parents, grown men or women or anyone who hurt you in the past?

....

....

....

....

....

41. Would you genuinely like to be delivered completely of these feelings?

....

....

....

42. Would you like to put this experience behind you and move forward?

....

....

....

....

....

PRAYER FOR YOUR PHYSICAL/EMOTIONAL HEALING AND TOTAL DELIVERANCE FROM PAST HURTS: If your answer to these questions is yes, then pray this prayer with me right now:

'Father, I come to you in the Name of Jesus, the Name which is above every name (Philippians 2:9-11) such as anger, hatred, revenge, bitterness, unforgiveness, resentment, and any negative feelings I have had towards those who have hurt me in the past in any way, shape or form. I confess and ask for your forgiveness for harbouring these feelings and I receive my forgiveness and cleansing by your blood now in the Name of Jesus according to 1 John 1:9 and I sincerely and wholeheartedly forgive them who have hurt me and wounded me in the past now. I receive your healing, deliverance, encouragement and full assurance of recovery from past hurts now and I receive the comforting, counselling power of the Hoy spirit now in Jesus' Name. For total recovery, I choose by faith from now to bless those who curse me, love my enemies, do good to those who have hated me, pray for those who have despitefully used me and persecuted me and bless those who have cursed me or will ever curse me (Matthew 5:44). This I do in the precious Name of Jesus and by the power of the Holy Spirit and receive a new beginning now in my life. Amen!'

FOR SALVATION: If you are not saved or born again yet, then pray this prayer now as well to be gloriously saved: 'Father, I thank you for sending Jesus to die for me and be raised from the dead. I believe it with my heart and confess it with my mouth (Romans 10:9-10). I ask for your forgiveness and receive you as my Lord and personal Saviour. I thank you for saving me in Jesus' Name; fill me with your Holy Spirit now with the evidence of the outflowing of the heavenly language from my spirit - speaking in tongues. I receive this gift and completeness now in Jesus' Name. Amen!'

NEW BEGINNING:

NOW,

43. What kind of husband or wife would you like to be and why?

....

....

....

....

....

44. What kind of parent would you like to be and why?

....

....

....

....

45. What would you like to do better than your parents did?

....

....

....

....

46. When you reach the end of your life, what do you want to look back on and say you have accomplished?

....

....

....

....

....

47. What do you think the special responsibilities and privileges of men are?..

....

....

....

48. What do you think the special responsibilities of and benefits of women are?

....

....

....

....

49. If you had the power to change anything about the way you look, what would it be and would you use it?

....

....

....

....

50. Are you a born-again Christian and how and when did you become a Christian?

....

....

....

51. Have you received the Holy Spirit Baptism? When?

....

....

....

TAKING AUTHORITY OVER DEMONIC INFLUENCES:

52. Were your parents or family, worshippers of idols, images or gods'?

....

....

....

53. Did your parents or any of your family members have any dealings with demonic spirits?

....

....

....

54. Did your parents of family members ever get involved in the occult or belong to a secret organisation like 'lodge', etc.?

....

....

....

....

55. Do they still worship idols, 'gods', and consult idols or demonic spirits before taking major decisions?

....

....

....

....

....

56. Do you visit those demonic sites yearly with your family or consult the 'gods' or do they still do?

....

....

....

....

What to DO: Stop it, dedicate your life to Christ, plead the blood of Jesus, break those covenants in Jesus' Name and claim exemption from every demonic consequence of those covenants, ceremonies, actions and associations now.

57. Are there any prevalent repetitive chronic diseases and mishaps like diabetes, barrenness, hypertension, high blood pressure, miscarriage, abortion, marriage failures, broken marriages and relationships, premature deaths, separations, divorce, etc.?

....

....

....

....

....

58. Were you dedicated to God or 'gods' when you were born?

....

....

....

....

59. Was libation poured out and ancestral spirits invoked or called upon to protect you before or when you were born or dedicated?

....
....
....
....
....

60. Do they still celebrate and participate in demonic rituals or festivals?

....
....
....
....
....

What to DO: Take authority over the devil, break his power and pull down this stronghold over your life and family in Jesus' Name by praying this prayer: 'Father I come in the Name of Jesus and God's Word in Luke 10:19, and declare I exercise authority over every power of Satan in Jesus' Name now. I render ineffective, null and void all agreements and covenants my parents made with the devil and ancestral spirits and render every such agreement, counsel and cord cancelled in Jesus Name. I apply the blood of Jesus over our past, present and future and declare we are free from Satan's hold in Jesus' Name. I overcome him by the blood and by the word of my testimony in Jesus' Name. I am no longer under the hold of Satan because, Jesus is the Lord of my life and family. Amen!

61. Do you know what your natural talent is? If yes, what is it or what are they?

....

....

....

....

62. What Christian activities have you pursued in your life?

....

....

....

63. What are your hobbies in general and which is your favourite?

....

....

....

....

64. How much scripture have you been able to memorise?

....

....

65. What major illnesses have you had?

....

....

66. Have you had an experience where you almost died? If yes, what was it and when was this?

....

....

....

INTERIM EXERCISE:

Grade Your Partner On The following:

Fair

Good

Excellent

67. His/Her leadership..

68. His/Her Diligence..

69. His/Her Commitment to Godly character................................

70. His/Her Gratefulness..

71. His/Her Timing..

72. His/Her Commitment to Submission/Headship..........................
....
....

73. What is Marriage? How do you understand this word and institution?

....
....
....
....
....

[For a better understanding of marriage, Order my books: 101 TIPS FOR A GREAT MARRIAGE; WHAT HUSBANDS WANT AND WHAT WIVES 'REALLY' WANT; NO RINGY, NO DINGY and 50 COMMON MISTAKES SINGLES MAKE from our bookshop or our website, www.houseofjudah.org.uk]

74. Why do you want to marry?

....
....
....
....
....

For REASONS WHY PEOPLE GET MARRIED, order my book: NO RINGY, NO DINGY from our bookshop or our website, www.houseofjudah.org.uk]

75. Why do you want to marry this particular man or woman and not someone else?

....
....
....

76. If you had another opportunity to marry again, will you still want to marry this same man, if you are a woman or this same woman if you are a man or someone else? Why? Think about it!

....
....
....
....
....
....
....

ALLOW ME TO DO A LITTLE TEACHING ON LOVE AND MARRIAGE

You often meet people who get involved in relationships and when you ask them, 'Why do you want to go out with him/her?' or 'Why do you want to date or get married to him/her?' most people would give you this same, monotonous, continuous, popular answer: 'Because, I love him' or 'Because, he loves me or she loves me.'

What I want to know is what kind of love are you talking about: 'lusty love', 'real love', 'sex love', 'family love', 'selfish me alone love', 'what I like love', 'unselfish love', 'sacrificial one-sided love', 'sharing love', 'give me, give me love', 'You treat me good, I stay with you love' or 'you treat me bad, I leave you love', 'she looks good love', 'he's macho love' .... which one are you talking about?

From the Greek language, there are four kinds of love.

Is it:

'agape love?',

'phileo love?',

'storge love?',

'eros love?'

WHICH ONE IS IT? Which One?

I want to know.

So, let's talk about:
'THIS LOVE BUSINESS'

We must deal with this subject because there is more to marriage than just love. You must look at love, yes, but beyond that you must look at issues like: Is it God's will for both of you to be together? Do you have the same or similar dreams, goals, vision? Are you compatible? Are your interests similar or complimentary? Is he or she for real? Are you both heading in the same or similar direction in life? Above all, both of you must have a deep understanding of the subject of love. A lack of understanding of this subject of love, which is not just a feeling, but, a discipline, is detrimental to a relationship. REMEMBER, LOVE IS NOT JUST A FEELING, BUT A DISCIPLINE. IT IS A CHOICE. IT'S A DECISION!

Say it to yourself several times. You must discipline yourself to love one person for life. It is not a feeling; it is a discipline; it is a major decision for life. That partner's life is not an apparatus to be used for performing experiments in your bedroom or sitting room or in the back seat of a car 'laboratory' like a guinea pig, as to whether it will work or it won't work. Neither is yours to play with. You are either in it for life or don't enter at all. That is why, this book is of such vital importance to read, study and understand before you plunge your head and whole life into this institution of marriage.

Marriage is an institution; You enter an institution not to change it, but to abide by its rules so you can benefit from what it has to offer you, to make you a better person, more effective and prominent, a master at what you do, to graduate with distinction, increase your salary scale, go into the world and make a great impact in life from what you discovered and applied and eventually recommend it to others. Choosing a wrong partner and entering into a lasting relationship for life, is like 'putting your head on the chopping block as sacrifice' as it were.

It is equivalent to placing your life into someone's hands here on earth, a fellow human being you have not investigated, researched, known or loved the right way – God's way, without knowing the full story, outcome or consequences.

Study And Discover What Marriage Really Is: Don't Just Accept What Others Are Saying.

Many are ignorant of what marriage really is. When we first got married we really didn't know much about marriage; all we knew was two people in love with each other, looking for freedom, have some children spend their lives together forever. What we did not know just like many was that there was the need to understand this subject of marriage itself. Many don't understand what it is. One of the major reasons why many seek separation or divorce at the sign of a little quarrel, disagreement or disappointment is a lack of knowledge and understanding of what they've gotten themselves into – the marriage. That's why God said about His people, in Hosea 4:6, 'My people are destroyed for lack of knowledge.' They have been taken into slavery and captivity because of their ignorance. What many don't know which they must know is that when you enter into a marriage, you are not committing yourself to the person per se, but to the very institution of marriage itself, so, you have to be very sure.

Marriage is an institution set by God with laws governing its operation. If you follow its laws and principles you will succeed but if you choose to go against the laid down guidelines set long before you were born and rebel, you will be cast out. You don't enter a natural institution such as a college or university like Oxford, Yale, Harvard or Morehouse and try to tell them what to do or try to change that institution to suit your desires. No, you tow the line and finish your course and graduate from that institution. Your commitment as long as you remain in that institution is to the institution and so is the marriage [institution].

So, no matter what happens, you are committed to what you committed your life to – the institution of marriage. Whenever you are entering marriage, commit yourself to the marriage, not the person, because people – everybody grows and change takes place. If you commit yourself to whoever you marry and think they will remain the same physically, you are deceived. LISTEN! People change, they do not look the same after a while, he/she may put on weight, may not be as slim as he/she was when you first met, the man may acquire what I call and used to have 'prosperity stomach', the woman's waste line might increase as well as the man, you may lose some hair, the woman's breast may sag, some teeth may fall out, some men's hair will grow from white, black or brown to grey and white and others may disappear completely.

What are you going to do when these natural changes take place? Are you going to leave? But, that is exactly what many selfish, ignorant, wicked people are doing today and I say categorically to everyone reading this book without reservation: 'THAT IS OUT OF ORDER!'

These are some of the reasons why we have the problems we see in our societies, communities, cities and nation today. My advice to you is: 'Don't add to this craziness.' LET'S RID OUR SOCIETY OF THIS IGNORANCE!

Because, entering marriage without a deep, conscious and deliberate understanding of this subject plus other factors aforementioned and more, can result in a life of unhappiness, regret, complaints, loss of appetite, frustration in life, contemplations of suicide, murder, temptations of infidelity outside the marriage, negative thoughts and possibilities of separation, divorce, etc. Those who suffer most are the children because children need both parents to grow up properly. Children who are raised by single parents are often deficient of the love, attention, discipline and certain traits and qualities that both parents should have given them from the same home, but for the grace of God. If it hadn't been for the grace of God, I would not have turned out the way I did. Thank God mama knew how to pray in her own way. Let's get this marriage thing right. As someone said, 'Marriage can be the next thing to heaven on earth, or the next thing to a hellish experience on earth of life imprisonment being served with hard labour.' That shall not be your portion. There is also an African saying which goes this way, 'When you are going into marriage 'ask' questions.' That is what this book has been written for: for your information, understanding and prevention of Satan's traps to destroy you leaving you unfulfilled in life.

Scripture says of counsel and safety the following:
Proverbs 24:6, "For by wise counsel thou shalt make thy war: and in multitude of counsellors there is safety."

Deuteronomy 32:28, "For they are a nation void of counsel, neither is there any understanding in them."

Proverbs 11:14, "Where no counsel is, the people fall: but in the multitude of counsellors there is safety."

Proverbs 21:31, "The horse is prepared against the day of battle: but safety is of the LORD."

Isaiah 11:2, "And the spirit of the LORD shall rest upon him, the spirit of wisdom and understanding, the spirit of counsel and might, the spirit of knowledge and of the fear of the LORD;"

Receive the spirit of wisdom and understanding, the spirit of counsel and might, the spirit of knowledge and of the fear of the Lord and May the Lord make you a person of quick understanding in your decision-making on this subject of love and marriage and in every other area of your life. Say Amen!

INSTRUCTION: Answer the following questions using your present understanding before you read the teaching on love and then answer the questions again accurately taking into consideration your new understanding of the subject on Love.

Questions Continued:

77. Woman, Do you love him?...
....

78. Man, Do you love her?...
....
....

79. Are you in love with each other?
....
....

80. How do you know?
....
....

81. Are you sure it's not just because of her looks now?
....
....

82. Are you sure it's not just because you want something from him/ her?
....
....

83. Gentleman, are you sure it's not just because of her short skirt and wonderful figure?
....
....
....
....

84. Lady, are you sure it's not because he has a lot of hair on his head now and on his body and his money? What if he loses his hair and money as soon as you get married?

....

....

....

....

85. Lady, are you sure it's not just because of the gifts he's been showering on you and the weekly visits to your favourite restaurant?

....

....

....

....

86. Gentleman, are you sure it's not just because of the food she cooks for you?

....

....

....

....

87. Lady, are you sure it's not just because of the nice compliments he's been paying you? How do you know?

....

....

....

88. Lady, are you sure it's not just because of his macho, masculine features?

....
....
....

89. Lady, are you sure it's not just because he makes you feel like a lady now?

....
....
....

90. Gentleman, are you sure it's not just because he shows you respect and makes you feel like a real man now?

....
....
....

91. What do you understand by the expression 'I am in love'?

....
....
....

92. What kind of love are you talking about? REASON being, there are four kinds of love from the Greek language; i.e. Eros, Storge, Phileo and Agape. So which one are you talking about?

....
....
....
....

TEACHING ON THE FOUR KINDS OF LOVE

Love in Greek.

The New Testament was translated from the Greek to English and from that Greek word, 'LOVE' comes four different meanings as follows: Your understanding of the following meanings of that one word will help you explain what you really mean when you say, 'I love you' or 'I'm in love with someone.'

Bible writers used four different Greek words for Love:

Eros - sexual love; from which you get the word erotic; erotic book shop, erotica; love in order to get something from you; this is physical love; married love; mutual desire between a man and a woman. This is love that is blessed of God and is found in Song of Solomon.

Storge (Pronounced storg'ay) – family love. Romans 12:10 says we are to treat Christians like we treat members of our own families – with respect.

Phileo (pronounced fil-eh' o) – the love of friendship, the affection we feel for people in friendly relationships. Phileo is a word that has to do with feelings; feelings for people; is a word for friendship love;

warm affectionate love of friends; how to be affectionate. Love because of friendship; Phileo also has an element of giving and receiving, an exchange, directly or indirectly.

Agape – (pronounced ag-ah' pay) divine love; love in spite of; unconditional love; agape is the kind of love that just gives and gives and gives never really asking for anything in return. That is God's divine kind of love for us which we must have for humanity. Some Philologists (those who deal with words) believe that the Greek words, eros, storge and phileo – are selfish.

- They say that **eros** is selfish because the man who loves his wife is actually loving himself and that when he looks into her eyes, he sees a reflection of himself.

- They say also that **storge** is selfish because the man who loves his family is invariably going to benefit from them, so he looks after his family knowing they will also look after him.

- They say that **phileo** has an element of giving, but also receiving. As a person loves his mate, his family and his friends, he is asking for something in exchange, either directly or indirectly.

- **Agape**, however is unselfish. It is the totally unselfish love of God toward His people; it gives and gives and keeps on giving never really asking for anything in exchange. It is a beautiful concept of love not based on emotions or feelings; it is actually a love by choice, a love that doesn't look for affinity and gives us the ability to love even what is unlovely, or the unlovable; it always has the best interest of the other person. GOD DOESN'T CHANCE TO LOVE US; HE CHOOSES TO LOVE US and so must we as Born-Again Christians.

LOVE IS A CHOICE; IT IS A DISCIPLINE, WE CHOOSE TO LOVE INSPITE OF. LOVE IS A DECISION

In summary:

Agape is the divine love, has the best interest of the other

Phileo is the love of friendship or brotherly love,

Storge is the love of family, and

Eros is the love of man for woman

QUESTION:

'What kind of Love do I need then?' you may ask.

ANSWER:

The Kind Of Love Everyone Needs In Order To Have a Successful, Happy, Fruitful, Secure, Sustaining, & Satisfying Marriage & Family Life Is - What I Call: The COMBINATION LOVE ANOINTING Or THE LOVE COMBINATION ANOINTING.

What I mean by Love Combination Anointing is, all the four kinds of love integrated to work together, hand in hand for fulfilment. This is not an either/or proposition by asking what is your preference or choice such as do you want to choose an affectionate love for people and friends or emotional love based on considerations and the act of the will or loving in spite of. There isn't just a single choice to be made. All of the four kinds of love are involved, are crucial and an absolute necessity. Let's look at the various combinations and how they work as we deliberately put them together and work them.

Agape & Eros

The fact is that **Eros** wanes because it is part of the ageing process. Without **agape,** the two have nothing in common. It takes more than **eros** to hold a marriage together. In fact, the waning of **eros** through the aging process can be an intimidating experience for the non-Christian male, which may result in him being anxious, fretful and worried about his sexual performance. But the beautiful thing about the Christian marriage is that the partners are not intimidated, anxious or worried about the aging process and the waning of **eros** because each one has one main thought in mind - **agape.** In the Christian, as **eros** wanes, **agape** gets better and better. The Christian husband and wife are looking out for each other's best interests. A blend of agape and eros develops an ingredient in marriage that non-Christians simply don't have. **Agape** makes a husband abstain from causing harm abuse, or being critical or condemnatory of his wife.

Agape and Storge

Agape adds a remarkable quality to storge the family life. A man with agape will not hurt or tear apart his family but rather look out for his family, protect, defend and provide for them. That is what happens when agape is added and works side by side with storge. **Storge** coupled with **agape** will cause parents to abstain from divorce because of its devastating emotional, physical, destructive, psychological and long-term negative effects, on the future security and stability of the family and more especially the children. **Agape** makes the parents conscious and curious to know where and how the children are at all times, to protect them, shield them from negative outside influences which can cause a loss of life. Storge says, 'If I have to put my life down to protect my family, I will.' **Agape** puts the family in proper perspective devoid of violence, insults, harm and danger.

Agape and Phileo

Some people choose to befriend us for selfish reasons, so we can add something to their lives. That is a one-sided kind of relationship. But phileo says you are not an object or an apparatus for experimentation to get what I want or what you want or a person who exists just for the pleasure of another. Agape and phileo together form a tie and a pact that will hold a friendship together no matter what happens. Scripture says in Proverbs 17:17, 'a friend loveth at all times.' When God gives you a friend with agape, that person will love you through thick and thin. He will stay with you, whether you are winning or losing, living or dying, in sickness and in health, working or redundant or unemployed, rich or poor; they feel what you feel; here is a friend that sticketh closer than a brother.

SUMMARY

Agape and eros in a marriage makes it a Christian marriage – an unselfish, thoughtful, loving, considerate marriage union.

Agape and storge in a family makes it a Christian family – a family that is not a civil war or a contest or a volcano ready to erupt or explode, but a family that is solid and strong, a house built on the firm foundation of God's love and His word.

Agape and phileo in a friendship makes it a friendship that is based not on external considerations. It is a friendship that will weather the storms, the adversities, and the setbacks in life – a friendship that will survive no matter how strong the wind is blowing or the earthquakes, or hurricanes of life. Agape is available in all the relationships of life because Romans 5:5 says it is shed abroad in our hearts by the Holy Ghost.

PRAYER:
Pray this prayer of dedication:

'Lord, your agape love is shed abroad in my heart. What I need and my marriage relationship, friendship relationships and family relationships need is more of your agape love, so I can improve and excel in every relationship I have. Agape will place an unselfish, sacrificial element in my marriage. It will strengthen my family and put solidarity in my friendships to keep them from being exploitative and manipulative.

I pray, Lord, that You will work to develop Your agape love in me, to make me what you want me to be, so that Your love shows through every area of my life for all to see and benefit from. I thank You for answered prayer in Jesus' Name. Amen.'

I trust that your understanding of the above explanation and teaching on love will help you to answer the question on the kind of love you say you have for your partner accurately.

Questions Continued:
HAVE YOU BOTH DISCUSSED THE FOLLOWING BEFORE?
93. The crucial role of friendship in marriage?……......………….......
94. Companionship in marriage?…………...........………….......…..
95. Pleasure in marriage?……………………........…....…….......….
96. Completeness in marriage?…………...........…………….......…...
97. Fruitfulness in marriage?…………………….......................……
98. Protection in marriage?……………………….......……….......…
99. How marriage illustrates Christ and the Church?

....

....…...................................

What will be your response when she:
100. Rehearses your "forgiveness" failures?

....

.............................…...

....…..

101. Does not perform her responsibilities at home?

....
....
....

102. Has undefined expectation (Is never pleased and has no respect or admiration for you?)

....
....
....
....

103. Resists your leadership?

....
....
....

104. Lacks confidence in your decisions?

....
....
....

105. Is ungrateful?

....
....
....

106. Fails to build loyalty for you in your children?

....
....
....
....

107. Exposes your marriage problems to outsiders?

....

....

....

108. Is inflexible to things you consider are your priorities?

....

....

....

109. When she repeatedly misunderstands what you are trying to say?

....

....

....

What will be your response when He:

110. Does not pay attention to you in public?

....

....

....

111. Fails to be a spiritual leader or decisive?

....

....

....

112. Allows problems to continue and even get worse?

....

....

....

113. Does not support you in disciplining the children?

....

....

....

114. Spends extra money on things he enjoys at the expense of the family?

....

....

....

115. Does not accept himself i.e. suffers from insecurity?

....

....

....

116. Praises or admires other women?

....

....

....

117. Verbalizes love [tells you he loves you] only when he has a physical or sexual relationship with you?

....

....

....

118. Forgets special occasions like your anniversary, birthday, Valentine's Day, etc?

....

....

....

119. Does not praise you for the specific jobs you do so well?

....

....

....

120. Is not alert to the danger you are facing?

....

....

....

121. Neglects urgent home needed repairs?

....

....

....

122. Does not have good manners?

....

....

....

123. Lusts after other women?

....

....

....

....

....

124. Loses his temper and does not ask you for forgiveness?

....

....

....

....

125. Have you discussed how to treat your in-laws, such as whether they'll come and stay with you or not if they are dependent on you and what was the conclusion?

....

....

....

....

126. Have you discussed how much to give to your parents or dependents each month and still be able to meet your budget as a newly married couple?

....

....

....

....

....

127. Have you thought of and discussed what percentage of your income together will go into your joint account?

....

....

....

....

128. How much have you talked about the issues that arise after marriage? (For example, where are we at this point in the relationship?)

....

....

....

....

129. Is there any impediment to this marriage? (Such as: resistance from parents, divorce, pregnancy, previous abortion, children from previous relationship or marriage, etc.? If any, what has been done about it?)

....
....
....
....
....

130. Do you understand Christian Marriage as regards submission to each other? [If not, read 1 Peter Chapter 3 & 1 Corinthians 13 and order my books: 101 Tips for a great marriage, WHAT HUSBANDS WANT AND WHAT WIVES 'REALLY' WANT from www. houseofjudah.org.uk]

....
....
....
....
....

131. Suppose you love each other and God says, 'no, you are not meant for each other, don't get married', what will you do?

....
....
....
....
....

133. How do you know it is the will of God for you to marry your partner?

....
....
....
....
....

134. Is it God's perfect timing for you to get married? How do you know?

....
....
....
....
....

135. Do you spend much time in prayer together?

....
....
....
....
....

136. Are you willing to wait until your marriage has been blessed, / consummated by the church before you come together for sexual union (have sex or make love)?

....
....
....

[Order my books: 50 Common Mistakes Singles Make; NO RINGY, NO DINGY; 101 Tips for a great marriage; What husbands want and what wives 'really' want from our website, www.houseofjudah. org.uk]

137. If not, why not?

....
....
....
....

138. Have you been petting or waiting till the D-day?

....
....
....
....

139. Are you aware that prevention is better than cure?

....
....
....
....

140. How sure are you that your partner will remain a Christian and committed to this marriage after you get married?

....
....
....
....

141. How do you know your partner will attend the same church with you after you are married; it could be he/she is going to the same church with you now because he/she wants you desperately?

....
....
....

142. How do you know he/she won't change his/her mind after 'his/her hands have reached their back' i.e. they've gotten what they want?

....
....
....

143. Are you even sure he will continue to go to church with you after you get married?

....
....
....

144. What are your temperaments?

....
....
....
....
....

145. Why do you want to get married? Reasons!

....
....
....

146. Do you like each other? [This question is asked on the premise/assumption that both of you are already in love]

....

....

....

147. What irritates you most in his/her conduct?

....

....

....

148. Are you pleased or delighted with each other's manners [i.e. eating habits, sloppy, etc.] or embarrassed?

....

....

....

....

149. Do you treat strangers better than you treat your family members?

....

....

....

....

....

150. How do you treat your father and mother? [Because that says a lot about how you will treat your spouse]

....

....

....

151. What is your attitude towards your prospective in-laws? [In other words do you like or get on well with them or not?]

....

....

....

....

152. Are you easily offended? [Are you over-sensitive to certain remarks?]

....

....

....

....

153. Do you have a sense of humour? [It is said that comics have lasting marriages]

....

....

....

....

....

154. Do you believe anyone outside of your marriage should help you financially?

....

....

....

....

....

155. What is your attitude about your wife working outside the home? [i.e. engaging in full-time or part-time employment to support your/ the family]

....
....
....
....

156. Who will handle the cheque book [finances] or keep the books / records and balances when you get married and why?

....
....
....
....
....

157. Are you going to pull all your resources together? [REMEMBER: separate accounts suggest possible problems]

....
....
....
....

158. How generous are you?

....
....
....
....
....

159. What is your attitude towards debt?

....

....

....

....

160. What plans do you have in mind in the area of budgeting?

....

....

....

....

161. How will you handle reverses such as unemployment, redundancies, sickness, debt, etc.?

....

....

....

....

162. Where will you live after you are married? [House, apartment, flat, bungalow, city, outskirts, suburbs, village i.e. (room and geography)]

....

....

....

....

163. Do you know the difference between sex and love?

....

....

....

164. What will you do when you discover that one partner is more highly sexed than the other? Will that create any problems and if so how will you deal with such a situation?

....
....
....
....

165. What books have you read or CDS/tapes have you listened to or films or videos/DVDS have you watched on the subject of marriage in general?

....
....
....
....

166. What will you do when you suspect or discover that your partner is romantically interested in another person?

....
....
....
....

167. When do you plan to have a child and if so how many children do you have in mind? [You need to discuss this at length]

....
....
....
....

168. What do you feel or think about birth control? Are you well-advised on this subject?

....

....

....

....

169. Are you flexible or rigid?

....

....

....

....

170. Do you have the same or similar interests in books, films, music, sports, games, church, athletics, education, career goals, food, leisure, etc.?

....

....

....

....

171. What is your attitude towards household chores such as washing dishes, mowing the lawns, ironing, dusting, vacuum cleaning, tidying up, dressing beds, cooking, etc.?

....

....

....

172. What does John expect of Mary? [REMEMBER: Unrealistic or Idealistic expectations causes problems]

....

....

....

173. What does Mary expect of John? [REMEMBER: Unrealistic or Idealistic expectations causes problems]

....

....

....

....

174. From John's perspective or point of view, what does he think Mary expects of him?..

....

....

....

175. From Mary's perspective or point of view, what does she think John expects of her?

....

....

....

....

176. Do you classify your success or failure as the success or failure of both of you or theirs and why is that so?

....

....

....

177. How will you handle each other's differences and contradictions? [Because, they exist]

....
....
....
....

178. Do you believe in careful, sensitive listening?

....
....
....

179. Do you believe in talking over issues and sharing in the decision-making for the family?

....
....
....
....

180. Do you believe in counselors helping you to solve your problems, challenges or issues? If not, why and if yes, sometimes or always?

....
....
....
....

181. What are your short-term and long-term goals or aspirations?

....
....
....
....

182. When was the last time you had a physical check-up and what were the results?

....
....
....
....

183. Where do you intend to go to church – his church or her church after you settle down as a married couple? [You need to discuss and make a concrete decision on this issue during your courtship before you get married.]

....
....
....
....

184. How will you treat religious differences or beliefs between you, if any?

....
....
....
....

185. Are you willing to commit each other to God to make both of you what He wants you to be for Himself and each other and not try to change each other to suit your aspirations for each other?

....
....
....
....

186. Do you understand that leadership, in the Biblical sense, is gentle, considerate, sacrificial and loving? How will you apply this principle in your marriage?

....

....

....

....

187. Do you recognize your equality before God and each other?

....

....

188. Do your parents, friends and relatives favour this marriage?

....

....

....

189. Have you made all the arrangements for the engagement and the wedding?

....

....

....

....

190. Is there anything about you that your fiancé (e) should know that you have not told him or her as we approach these additional sensitively dangerous must-ask questions?

....

....

....

....

OTHER ADDITIONAL QUESTIONS YOU MAY OR MAY NOT ASK, BUT HAVE TO [MUST] ASK.

THE FOLLOWING QUESTIONS ARE QUESTIONS THAT SOME WOULD NEVER DARE TO ASK! BUT FAILURE TO ASK THEM AND GET THE TRUTH FROM THE ONSET FROM YOUR PARTNER DURING THE DATING AND COURTSHIP PERIOD CAN BE VERY DEVASTATING LATER ON. BECAUSE, THESE DAYS YOU CANNOT BE NAÏVE TO THINK THAT IT'S ONLY WOMEN WHO ARE LUSTING AFTER YOUR HUSBANDS OR MEN AFTER YOUR WIVES. THERE ARE ALSO MEN LUSTING AFTER YOUR HUSBANDS AND WOMEN LUSTING AFTER YOUR WIVES. THEY ARE CALLED 'GAYS' - HOMOSEXUALS AND LESBIANS. ('Secret Descendants' of Sodom & Gomorrah)

WARNING: FOR THOSE OF YOU WHO TAKE YOUR WIVES OR HUSBANDS FOR GRANTED, REMEMBER THAT SOME SO-CALLED 'CHRISTIAN MEN' ARE 'BELIEVING GOD' FOR YOUR WIVES, AND SOME SO-CALLED 'GAY CHRISTIAN MEN' ARE 'BELIEVING GOD' FOR YOUR HUSBANDS WHILST OTHER SO-CALLED 'BELIEVING CHRISTIAN WOMEN' ARE 'BELIEVING GOD' FOR YOUR HUSBANDS AND OTHER 'GAY LESBIAN SO-CALLED CHRISTIAN WOMEN' ARE 'BELIEVING GOD' FOR YOUR WIVES.

THIS SICK BUT TRUE PASSIONS AND TWISTED DESIRES DO OCCUR AND CAN LEAD TO SHOCK, SUSPICION AND HEART ATTACKS. TO DISCOVER THAT YOU ARE MARRIED TO OR LIVING WITH SOMEONE WITH SUCH FEELINGS FOR ANOTHER PERSON OF THE SAME SEX, OR ADDICTED TO PONOGRAPHY, MASTURBATION OR WORSE STILL IS A PAEDOPHILE CAN BE OVERWHELMING, VERY DESTRUCTIVE AND DEVASTATING.

THESE ARE THEREFORE 21st CENTURY, MUST-ASK QUESTIONS, WHICH ARE SERIOUS, NECESSARY, UNAVOIDABLE, 'ANAGKAZO', 'BIAZO', 'ANAIDEIA', COMPULSORY QUESTIONS THAT YOU CANNOT AFFORD TO OVERLOOK OR SHY AWAY FROM ASKING MORE ESPECIALLY IF THE ANSWER TO ANY OF THEM IS YES! THIS MUST BE DONE WITH EXPERT PASTORAL GUIDANCE, COUNSEL AND SUPPORT.

The questions are as follows:

191. Is there anything else I need to know about you that I don't know yet, such as addiction to pornography, [both children and adult]? What are the bad habits/weaknesses/secret sins that you've been dealing with in secret such as addiction to masturbation, homosexuality, prostitution, alcohol, gambling, drugs, compulsive or excessive buying, etc.? Are you in debt to your 'eyeballs', etc.? Are you a paedophile? Are you on the paedophile or sex offenders register? Have you been arrested before, served a jail sentence before? If so,

when, where and what for?

....
....
....
....
....
....
....
....

192. Is there anything in your past or present that you cannot tell me or are ashamed of or afraid to tell me, such as: Are you 'gay' [a homosexual or a lesbian]? As a man, are you more inclined to men romantically or do you prefer men to women, sexually, i.e. would you prefer to date, kiss, pet, marry, sleep with a fellow man and have anal sex with a him than normal love-making with your wife [a woman] such as the men in Sodom & Gomorrah (Genesis 18 & 19) and some in our day]? On the other hand, if you are a woman, would you prefer to date, kiss, pet, marry or sleep with or have 'sex' such as oral sex with a fellow woman than a man [your husband]? Are you sure you are not just marrying me for prestige to cover hidden bad habits and preserve your name, reputation or image?

....
....
....
....
....
....
....

193. Are you keeping any secrets from me that I might find out later that might jeopardize our relationship?

....

....

....

....

194. Have you been thoroughly frank with me about everything or at least about most things?

....

....

....

....

195. Are you sure you did not choose me because I look like your first or former boyfriend or girlfriend or your mother or father or favourite uncle or aunt?

....

....

....

....

....

196. Are you really a man or woman? Have you ever had a sex change, a breast implant or a facelift? If so, where, when and why?

....

....

....

....

197. Have you been married before? Were you ever separated, divorced or widowed? Do you have a wife or husband or children anywhere else that I do not know of?

....
....
....
....

198. Were you ever adopted by anyone or raised in a foster home?

....
....
....
....

199. Are you sure you are not just marrying me out of a rebound to prove to your former husband or wife that you are still attractive or out of spite?

....
....
....
....

200. Do you have any secret children from a previous relationship or marriage that I have not met; if yes, how many and how young or how old are they?

....
....
....
....

POIGNANT REMINDERS:

You must look at love, yes, but beyond that you must look at vision, compatibility, interests, as to whether your partner is heading in the same or similar direction in life as you.

A lack of understanding of this subject of love, which is not just a feeling, but, a discipline is very detrimental to a meaningful and lasting relationship.

Remember: Love is not a feeling; it is a discipline.

You must discipline yourself to love one person for life.

Your partner's life is not an apparatus to be used for performing experiments in a bedroom, backseat, sitting room 'laboratory' like a guinea pig, as to whether it will work or it won't work. Neither is yours to play with. You are either in it for life or don't enter at all.

Marriage is an institution; You enter an institution not to change it, but to abide by its rules so you can benefit from what it has to offer you, to make you a better person, more effective and prominent, a master at what you do, to graduate with distinction, increase your salary scale, go into the world and make a great impact in life from what you discovered and applied and eventually recommend it to others.

Commit your life to the marriage not the person per se. So that when something happens you stay with the institution.

'Marriage can be the next thing to heaven on earth, or the next thing to a hellish experience on earth of life imprisonment being served with hard labour.'

Your understanding of the four different Greek words for 'Love' will help you explain what you really mean when you say, 'I love you' or 'I'm in love with someone.'

Bible writers used four different Greek words for Love:
Eros - sexual love; from which you get the word erotic; erotic book shop, erotica; love in order to get something from you; this is physical love; married love; mutual desire between a man and a woman. This is love that is blessed of God and is found in Song of Solomon.

Storge (Pronounced storg'ay) – family love. Romans 12:10 says we are to treat Christians like we treat members of our own families – with respect.

Phileo (pronounced fil-eh' o) – the love of friendship, the affection we feel for people in friendly relationships. Phileo is a word that has to do with feelings; feelings for people; is a word for friendship love; warm affectionate love of friends; how to be affectionate. Love because of friendship; Phileo also has an element of giving and receiving, an exchange, directly or indirectly.

Agape – (pronounced ag-ah' pay) divine love; love in spite of; unconditional love; agapc is the kind of love that just gives and gives and gives never really asking for anything in return. That is God's divine kind of love for us which we must have for humanity.
Love is a choice; it is a discipline. We choose to love people in spite of who they are, their background or what they've done.

In summary:
Agape is the divine love, has the best interest of the other
Phileo is the love of friendship or brotherly love,
Storge is the love of family, and
Eros is the love of man for woman

QUESTION: What kind of Love do we need to experience a great successful, happy, fruitful, secure, lasting, sustaining and satisfying marriage and family.

ANSWER: It is all the four kinds of love integrated to work together, hand in hand for fulfilment. This is not an either/or proposition by asking what is your preference or choice such as do you want to choose an affectionate love for people and friends or emotional love based on considerations and the act of the will or loving in spite of. There isn't just a single choice to be made. All of the four kinds of love are involved, are crucial and an absolute necessity. Let's look at the various combinations and how they work as we deliberately put them together and work them.

Agape & Eros
The fact is that Eros wanes because it is part of the ageing process. Without agape, the two have nothing in common. It takes more than **eros** to hold a marriage together. In fact, the waning of eros through the aging process can be an intimidating experience for the non-Christian male, which may result in him being anxious, fretful and worried about his sexual performance. But the beautiful thing about the Christian marriage is that the partners are not intimidated, anxious or worried about the aging process and the waning of eros because each one has one main thought in mind - agape. In the Christian, as **eros** wanes, agape gets better and better. The Christian husband

and wife are looking out for each other's best interests. A blend of agape and **eros** develops an ingredient in marriage that non-Christians simply don't have. Agape makes a husband abstain from causing harm abuse, or being critical or condemnatory of his wife.

Agape and Storge

Agape adds a remarkable quality to storge the family life. A man with agape will not hurt or tear apart his family but rather look out for his family, protect, defend and provide for them. That is what happens when agape is added and works side by side with storge. Storge coupled with agape will cause parents to abstain from divorce because of its devastating emotional, physical, destructive, psychological and long-term negative effects, on the future security and stability of the family and more especially the children. Agape makes the parents conscious and curious to know where and how the children are at all times, to protect them, shield them from negative outside influences which can cause a loss of life. Storge says, 'If I have to put my life down to protect my family, I will.' Agape puts the family in proper perspective devoid of violence, insults, harm and danger.

Agape and Phileo

Some people choose to befriend us for selfish reasons, so we can add something to their lives. That is a one-sided kind of relationship. But phileo says you are not an object or an apparatus for experimentation to get what I want or what you want or a person who exists just for the pleasure of another. Agape and phileo together form a tie and a pact that will hold a friendship together no matter what happens. Scripture says in Proverbs 17:17, 'a friend loveth at all times.' When God gives you a friend with agape, that person will love you through thick and thin. He will stay with you, whether you are winning or losing, living or dying, in sickness and in health, working or redundant or unemployed, rich or poor; they feel what you feel; here is a friend that sticketh closer than a brother.

SUMMARY

Agape and eros in a marriage makes it a Christian marriage – an unselfish, thoughtful, loving, considerate marriage union.

Agape and storge in a family makes it a Christian family – a family that is not a civil war or a contest or a volcano ready to erupt or explode, but a family that is solid and strong, a house built on the firm foundation of God's love and His word.

Agape and phileo in a friendship makes it a friendship that is based not on external considerations. It is a friendship that will weather the storms, the adversities, and the setbacks in life – a friendship that will survive no matter how strong the wind is blowing or then earthquakes, or hurricanes of life.

Agape is available in all the relationships of life because Romans 5:5 says it is shed abroad in our hearts by the Holy Ghost.

PRAYER:

Pray this prayer of dedication:

'Lord, I'm a candidate for **agape**. What I need and my marriage relationship, friendship relationships and family relationships need is more of Your **agape** love, so I can improve and excel in every relationship I have. **Agape** will place an unselfish, sacrificial element in my marriage. It will strengthen my family and put solidarity in my friendships to keep them from being exploitative and manipulative. I pray, Lord, that You will work to develop Your **agape** love in me, to make me what you want me to be, so that Your love shows through every area of my life for all to see and benefit from. I thank You for answered prayer in Jesus' Name. Amen.'

The End For Now!

[For a better understanding of marriage and to build solid, great, lasting and fulfilling relationships, order the entire RELATIONSHIPS PACK comprising this book and the following books: 101 TIPS FOR A GREAT MARRIAGE; WHAT HUSBANDS WANT AND WHAT WIVES 'REALLY' WANT; NO RINGY, NO DINGY; 50 COMMON MISTAKES SINGLES MAKE and CDS and DVDS from our bookshop or our website, www.houseofjudah.org.uk]

THE GREATEST GIFT

If you have never met or experienced a definite encounter with Jesus Christ, you can know Him today. You can make your life right with Him by accepting Him as your personal Lord and Saviour by praying the following prayer out loud where you are. Pray this prayer with me now:

PRAYER FOR SALVATION: 'O God, I ask you to forgive me for my sins. I believe You sent Jesus to die on the cross for me and confess it with my mouth. I receive Jesus Christ as my personal Lord and Saviour and confess Him as Lord of my life and I give my life willingly to Him now. Thank you Lord for saving me and for making me a new person in Jesus' Name, (2 Corinthians 5:17) Amen.'

If you prayed this prayer, you have now become a child of God (John 1:12) and I welcome you to the family of God. Please let me know about your decision for Jesus by writing to me. I would like to send you some free literature to help you in your new walk with the Lord.

So please write to me at the following address:

Correspondence address:
Bishop Michael Hutton-Wood,
House of Judah (Praise) Ministries
P. O. Box 1226,
Croydon. CR9 6DG. UK.

Or call:
Within the UK:
0208 689 6010, 07956 815 714
Outside the UK:
+44 208 689 6010, +44 7956 815 714

Alternatively Email us at:
Email: info@houseofjudah.org.uk
michaelhutton-wood@fsmail.net
Or visit us at: Website: www.houseofjudah.org.uk

Watch our 24hour internet TV experience on
www.judahtv.org

OTHER BOOKS AND LEADERSHIP MANUALS BY AUTHOR

1. A Must For Every New Convert
2. You Need To Do The Ridiculous In Order To Experience The Miraculous
3. 175 Reasons Why You Cannot And Will Not Fail In Life
4. What To Do In The Darkest Hour Of Your Trial [125 Bible Truths You Must Know, BELIEVE, REMEMBER, CONFESS AND DO]
5. Why You should Pray And How You should Pray For Your Pastor and Your Church Daily
6. 200 Questions You Must Ask, Investigate And Know Before You Say 'I Do'
7. I Shall Rise Again
8. How to negotiate your desired future with today's currency
9. Leadership Secrets
10. Leadership Nuggets
11. Leadership Capsules
12. What is Ministry
13. Generating Finances For Ministry
14. 101 Tips For a Great Marriage
15. What Husbands Want And What Wives 'REALLY' Want
16. My Daily Bible Reading Guide.
17. Taking The Struggle Out Ministry
18. No Ringy, No Dingy
19. 50 Common Mistakes Single Make.

TRAINING MANUALS FOR IMPACTFUL LEADERSHIP & EFFECTIVE MINISTRY

Academy 101 [House Of Judah Academy Curriculum]

Ministry 101

Leadership 101

Kingdom Prosperity 101 From School Of Kingdom Prosperity & Financial Management

Pastoral Leadership 101 From School Of Impactful Pastoral Leadership

Prescriptions For Fulfilling Your Ministry

To order copies of any of these books, ministry or leadership manuals or for a product catalog of other literature, audiotapes and CDs, DVDs, write to: **Michael Hutton-Wood Ministries, P. O. Box 1226, Croydon. CR9 6DG. UK. or [in the UK call] - 0208 689 6010; [outside UK call] + 442086896010**

You can also place your order online as you visit our website: **www. houseofjudah.org.uk**

You can also email us at:

Email: **info@houseofjudah.org.uk;**

or **michaelhutton-wood@fsmail.net**

GLOBAL INITIATIVES AND MINISTRIES WITHIN THE MINISTRY

TV MINISTRY IN THE UK

Watch Leadership Secrets on KICC TV

SKY Channel 594

Tuesday & Thursday – 3pm & Saturday 5.30pm

Monday-Friday 2pm on FAITH TV

Sky channel 593 & Saturday 3.30pm

LOG ON AND WATCH OUR INTERNET TV PROGRAM on

WWW.JUDAHTV.ORG

Anytime - anywhere.

Featuring the:

Teaching Channel

Motivation Channel

Leadership Channel

Family/ Relationships Channel

Upcoming Events/ Products

WATCH US ON YouTube and AUDIO STREAMING

EVERY WEEK

@ www.houseofjudah.org.uk

PARTNERING WITH A GLOBAL MINISTRY WITHIN A MINISTRY

Michael Hutton-Wood Ministries (The HUTTON-WOOD WORLD OUTREACH MINISTRY) is the apostolic, missions, world outreach, and evangelistic wing of the House of Judah (Praise) Ministries with a mission to God's end time church and the nations of the earth. This ministry was born out of a strong God-given mandate to reach, touch and impact the nations of the earth with the gospel of Christ and bring back divine order, discipline, integrity, godly character, excellence and stability to God's people and God's house. It has a strong apostolic mandate to set in order the things that are out of order and lacking in the church [The Body of Christ] – (Titus 1:5).

Its mission is to save the lost at any cost, depopulate hell and populate heaven with souls that have experienced in full, the new birth, renewal of mind, to produce believers walking in the fullness of their Godly inheritance, divine health, prosperity and authority to take their homes, communities, cities and nations for Christ and occupy till Christ returns. It is to raise a people without spot, wrinkle or blemish. The man of God's passion and drive is that as truly as he lives, this earth shall be filled with the knowledge of the glory of the Lord as the waters cover the sea. His determination is not to rest, hold back or keep silent until he sees the body of Christ established as a praise in the earth. (Numbers 14:21; Habakkuk 2:14; Isaiah 62:6-7)

If you would like to join the faithful brethren and partners of this great ministry by becoming a partner as we believe God for ten thousand partners to partner with this vision prayerfully and financially, ask for a copy of the partners' club commitment card by writing to:

Michael Hutton-Wood Ministries
[Hutton-Wood World Outreach]
P. O. Box 1226, Croydon. Surrey.
CR9 6DG. UK.

Alternatively, you can send a monthly contribution by cheque payable to our ministry or donate online at www.houseofjudah.org.uk or request a direct debit mandate or standing order form from your bankers or us made payable to Michael Hutton-Wood Ministries. Call +44 [0] 208 689 6010 for more details. Philippians 4:19 be your portion and experience as you partner with this work and global mandate. Shalom!

GENERATIONAL LEADERSHIP TRAINING INSTITUTE
(The Leaders' Factory)

The Mandate: Raising Generational Leaders, Impacting Nations.

The Generational Leadership Training Institute (GLTI) is the Leadership training and mentoring wing of our ministry with a global mandate to raise leaders with a generational thinking mindset, not a now mentality and to fulfil the Law of Explosive Growth – To add growth, lead followers – To multiply, lead leaders.

This is a Bible College, Leadership Training Institute fulfilling the Matthew 9:37-38 mandate of developing and releasing labourers for the end time harvest. We offer fulltime and part time certificate, diploma, degree and short twelve-week courses in biblical studies, counselling, leadership, practical ministry and schools of prosperity. Its aim is to raise leaders who know and live not just by the anointing but by ministerial ethics, leaders who build with a long term mentality, who live today with tomorrow in mind. The mission of this unique educational and impartation institution is to transform followers into generational leaders and its motto is to raise leaders of discipline, integrity, godly character and excellence - D.I.C.E.

For correspondence, full time, part time, online courses, prospectus, fees and registration forms for the next course, call 0208 689 6010 or write to the Registrar, **GLTI, P. O. Box 1226, Croydon. CR9 6DG. UK or from outside UK call +44 208 689 6010.**

Additional information can be obtained from visiting our website www.houseofjudah.org.uk looking for THE LEADERS FACTORY.

Log on to www.judahtv.org for Leadership Secrets and other teaching.

This is a hutton-wood publication

LEADERS FACTORY INTERNATIONAL

MANDATE: 'In the business of training, developing and raising and releasing more leaders and leaders of leaders.'

'Leaders must be close enough to relate to others, but far enough ahead to motivate them.' – John Maxwell

'You must live with people to know their problems, and live with God in order to solve them.' – P. T. Forsyth

If you, your organisation, college, university, business or church would like to invite Dr. Michael Hutton-Wood for a Motivational-speaking, mentoring or leadership coaching engagement or to organize or hold a Leaders Factory seminar or conference, Leadership Development or Human Capital building seminar, Emerging leaders seminar, Management seminar, Business seminar, Effective people-management, Wealth-creation seminar or training for your workers, leaders, staff, ministers, employers, employees, congregation, youth, etc. you can contact us on 0208 689 6010 [UK]

+44208 689 6010 [OUTSIDE UK].

Alternatively by email at:
- info@houseofjudah.org.uk
- michaelhutton-wood@fsmail.net
or leadersfactoryinternational@yahoo.com
VISIT our website: www.houseofjudah.org.uk
You can watch our internet TV experience www.judahtv.org [Maximizing Destiny and Leadership Secrets].
This is a Hutton-Wood publication

MANDATE:
Releasing Potential - Maximizing Destiny
Raising Generational Leaders
- Impacting Nations

SIMPA
SCEPTRE INTERNATIONAL MINISTERS & PASTORS ASSOCIATION

This covenant mandate comes from Genesis 49:10: 'The sceptre [of Leadership] shall not depart from JUDAH, nor a lawgiver from between his feet, until Shiloh come and unto Him shall the gathering of the people be'

Other covenant scriptures backing this mandate are: Isaiah 55:4 & Titus 1:5. We have a leadership assignment to RAISE GENERATIONAL LEADERS TO IMPACT NATIONS BY DISCOVERING MEN/ WOMEN AND EMPOWERING THEM TO RELEASE THEIR POTENTIAL TO MAXIMIZE THEIR DESTINY.

SIMPA is a multi-cultural fellowship/network of diverse Christian leaders, pastors and ministers that recognize the need for fathering, covering and mentoring. The heartbeat of the man of God is to pour into the willing and obedient what has made him and keeps making him from what he's learnt from his father in the Lord, his teachers and mentors which is working for him and producing maximally. He said: 'I discovered this secret early: Not to learn from or follow those who make promises but from those who have obtained the promises, proofs and results. REMEMBER: YOU DON'T NEED TO MAKE NOISE TO MAKE NEWS. SO: FOLLOW NEWS-MAKERS NOT NOISE-MAKERS!'

These are a few of the mindsets of the man of God:

When the students are ready, the teacher will teach.

'YOU NEED FATHERS TO FATHER YOU TO GROW FEATHERS TO FLY.' – Bishop Oyedepo

'Without a father to father you, you can never grow feathers to fly and go further in life, than they went and accomplish more than they did.' – Michael Hutton-Wood

Don't raise money; raise men and you'll have all the money you need to accomplish your assignment.

There is no new thing under the sun – King Solomon

What you desire to attain, become and accomplish in life, someone has accomplished it – find them, follow them, learn from them, sow into them and their resource materials and you will do more than they did and get there faster.

Teachers, Trainers, Mentors and Fathers give you speed/acceleration in every field of endeavour.

Isaac Newton is known to have said the following:

'If I have seen further it has been by standing on the shoulders of those who have gone ahead of me.'

Variant translations: 'Plato is my friend, Aristotle is my friend, but my best friend is truth.'

'Plato is my friend — Aristotle is my friend — truth is a greater friend.'

'If I have seen further it is only by standing on the shoulders of giants.'

Without a reference you can never become a reference.

If you don't refer to anyone no one will refer to you.

Who laid / lays hands on you and what did / do they leave behind?

This is not a money-making venture but rather about covering and empowerment for fulfilment of destiny and assignment within time allocated.

The goal of SIMPA is to spiritually cover, strengthen, equip, empower, train, mentor and encourage and lift up the arms/hands of both emerging and active [full and part time] pastors, ministers and leaders and by so doing release them to fulfil their respective assignments both in ministry and the market place.

IF YOU WOULD LIKE TO BE A PART OF SIMPA, ASK FOR A REGISTRATION FORM & PAMPHLET FROM OUR INFORMATION DESK in House of Judah or email info@houseofjudah. org.uk or call [in the UK] 0208 689 6010 [outside UK call] + 44 208 689 6010 requesting for SIMPA registration form and pamphlet.

– SEE YOU ON TOP!

Shalom! – Bishop

PARTNERSHIP:

In the UK write or send cheque donations to:

Michael Hutton-Wood Ministries

P. O. Box 1226

Croydon. CR9 6DG. UK.

In the UK Call: 0208 689 6010; 07956 815 714

Outside the UK call: +44 208 689 6010;

+ 44 7956 815 714

Fax: +44 20 8689 3301

Email:

info@houseofjudah.org.uk

michaelhutton-wood@fsmail.net

leadersfactoryinternational@yahoo.com

judah@houseofjudah.freeserve.co.uk

Or visit or donate online at our secure

WEBSITE: www.houseofjudah.org.uk

Watch our 24 hour internet TV experience by logging on
anywhere - anytime @ www.judahtv.org

Michael & Bernice Hutton-Wood

BOOKS AND LEADERSHIP MANUALS
BY BISHOP MICHAEL HUTTON-WOOD

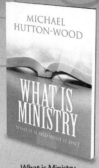

What is Ministry

My Daily Bible
Reading Guide

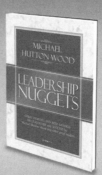

Leadership Nuggets

175 Reasons Why You Cannot
And Will Not Fail In Life

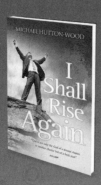

I Shall Rise Agian

Leadership Capsules

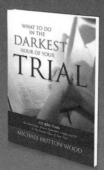

What To Do In The Darkest
Hour of Your Trial

Generating Finances
For Ministry

TRAINING MANUALS FOR IMPACTFUL LEADERSHIP & EFFECTIVE MINISTRY

OTHER BOOKS BY THE AUTHOR
- BISHOP MICHAEL HUTTON-WOOD -

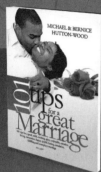
101 Tips For A Great Marriage

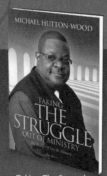
Taking The Struggle Out Of Ministry

What Husbands Want And What Wives 'REALLY' Want

50 Common Mistakes Singles Make

No Ringy, No Dingy

How To Negotiate Your Desired Future With Today's Currency

Leadership Secrets

You Need To Do The Ridiculous In Order To Experience The Miraculous

Why You Should Pray for your Pastor And For Your Church Daily

200 Questions You Must Ask, Investigate And Know Before You Say I Do

A Must For Every New Convert

FOR MORE INFORMATION AND TO ORDER ONLINE:
Please log on to www.houseofjudah.org.uk or call 02086896010 with your card details.